Bully Troubles

with

Leona Fiona

Written By: Susie Beinborn

Illustrated By: Anna Jenson

Leona Fiona is dedicated to my mom, Leona, who for all my life has been my "go to" person. My mom was amazing in sharing her wisdom, her love, and her childhood memories. She was always there for me, and I could always count on a story, a song, and a hug, no matter the day. I lost my mom this year to the Coronavirus, but before she left us (this book not yet ready for print), I read her the words and shared this all with her. She was nearing the end of her life here on earth--she wasn't talking anymore and her eyes mostly shut--yet I knew God was with us both that day, just by the way our hearts felt. Those days were "Heaven Sent!" I love you mom...more than donuts!

-November 2020

Little Leona Fiona is such a funny girl,

she always wears a ponytail with just a little curl.

Constantly chasing the boys, until she made them cry.

So Mama finally asked, "Leona Fiona, Why?"

"Why do you chase and be so mean?

I know this is not who you truly can be.

So explain to me dear why you act this way?

I will not allow this behavior!

This is SO NOT OKAY!"

"Well Mama," cried Leona Fiona. "They always
pick on me. They call me names and
make faces too, and push me into trees!
And Mama if that's not enough, the worst day
I feared...

...*Was when that little boy named Harry peed right*

in my ear!

"I was laying on the ground just playing hide and seek.

When he came upon me lying there, you know he's such a little creep!"

She looked somewhat green as she retold her story.

"Mama," she said, "I just wanted to throw up.

So that's when I chose to get even, Because I'd had ENOUGH!"

"Now Mama that is why he needs to learn a lesson.
Please understand my reasons, this is my confession.

He makes me super angry! I'd hit him with my fist,
and kick him with my boot if I knew I wouldn't
miss."

Mama said, "Oh my dear sweet child, what have you done?

But more importantly my dear, which way did those boys run?

I need to have a chat with them, I want to hear their reasons.

Do they think this is funny? Do they think it's all just teas'n?

Yes, Harry and the boys need to learn, and you my dear do too.

Because not one of you really have a clue."

"There are other ways to solve this, two wrongs don't make a right."

"You must understand that by continuing this behavior, you will have a sad, sad life."

"You are both fortunate, a whole life ahead of you.
So get your head on straight and take a different view.
Step back and contemplate, count your blessings
one by one.
All of you are wrong here, now can this
PLEASE be done!"

No more chasing and being mean, do I make myself clear?
And CERTAINLY no more nonsense of peeing in the ear!
You all have great qualities so open up your hearts, find the good in each other, please stop throwing darts.
Work things out, be friends, be the better soldier.
You will like the better you, you will thank me when you're older.

That Mama knew it best, knew it to be true.

From that point on, their friendship only grew.

CPSIA information can be obtained
at www.ICGtesting.com
Printed in the USA
BVHW022314130521
607264BV00002B/141